Stories
from the
Heart
of
God

Vol. 1

CREATION

Jacqie D'Bach

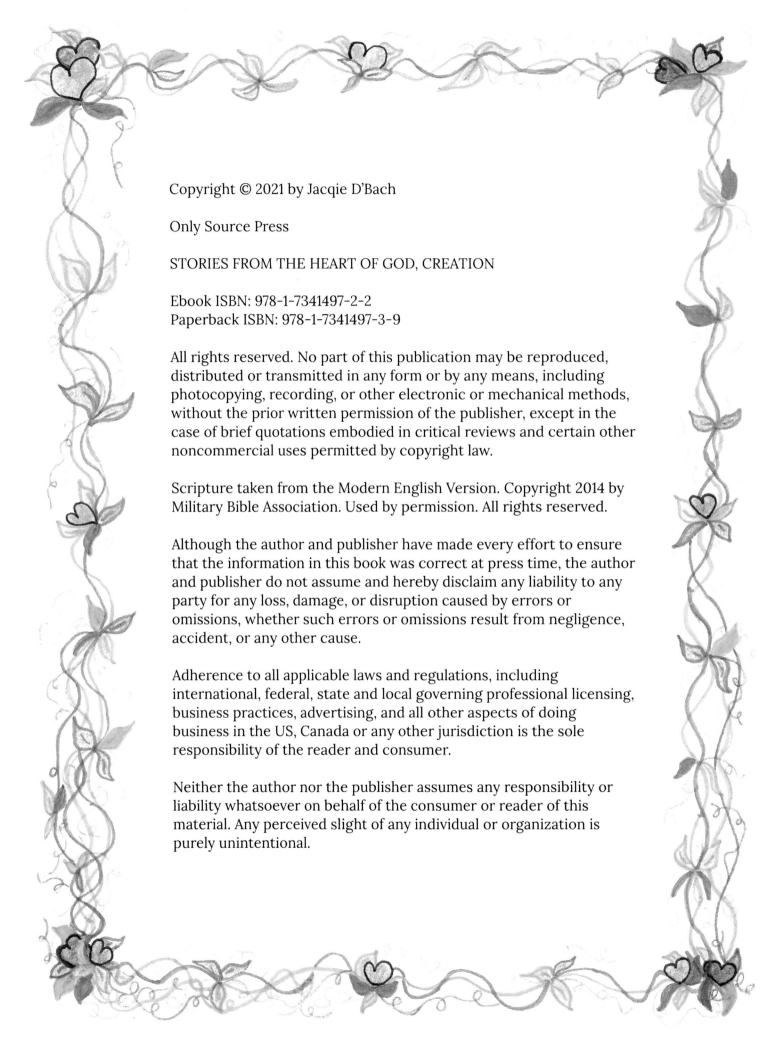

For: Ethan and Lincoln,
You two are just the inspiration I needed.
Thanks so much my little Buddies.
I love you.

Contents

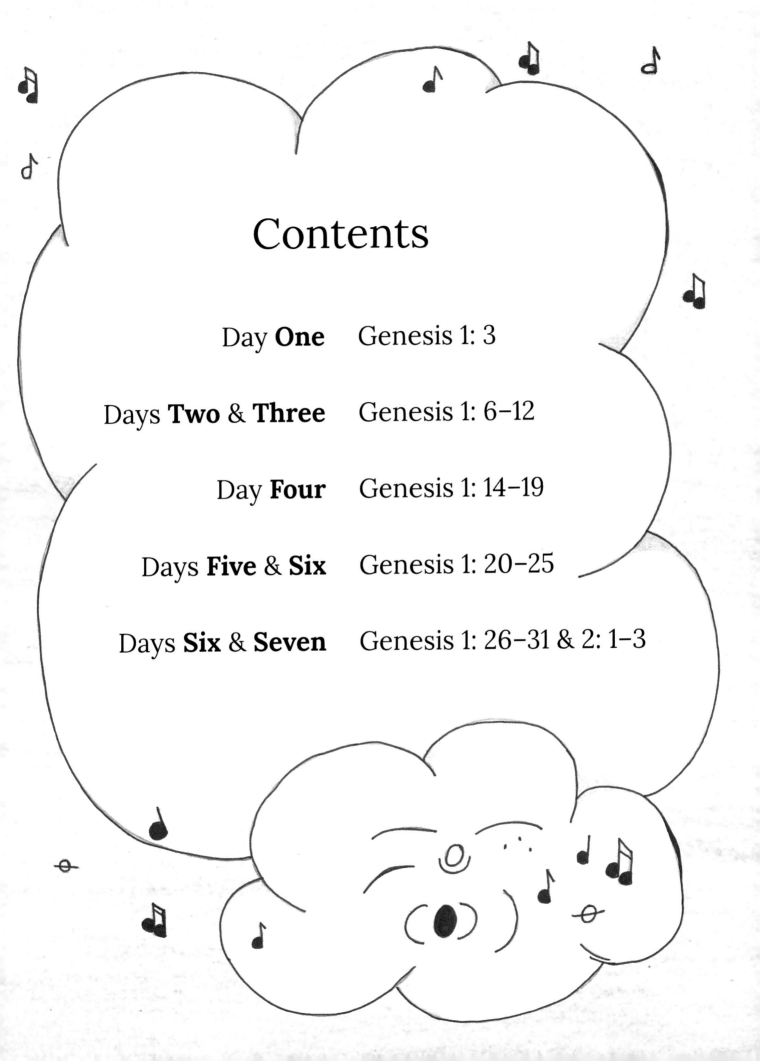

All things new at the start.
Gods' creation from His heart.

"Let there be light."
And so it was.
Day **One** passed by like still it does.

Find the number **One, 1**.

The sky was formed from great space. Day **Two** was gone without a trace.

Day **Three** brought mountains, rivers and trees and many pretty flowers for us to see.

Find the numbers **Two, 2** and **Three, 3**.

Then He hung the sun for day, so all little children could see to play.

For night the moon and stars were hung, 'cause that's when lullabies are sung.

Find the number **Four, 4**.

That was **Four**
and next comes **Five**,
when fish filled the water
and birds the sky.

On day **Six**;
furry, scaly, smooth and sleek;
animals were made,
it's almost complete.

Find the numbers **Five**, 5 and **Six**, 6.

Man was created
on day **Six**, as Well.
God saw His creation
and knew it was swell

At last day **Seven**
designed for rest.
Enjoy all things
with each given breath.

Find the numbers **Six, 6** and **Seven, 7.**

Dear (Insert your child's name here)

I am a prayer pillow.
I represent the heart of God.
Take me with you everywhere
Knowing that everywhere is our God.

On my back you'll find a pocket.
To place your many prayers.
I'm never full. There's always room
To share your joys and cares.

Our God is always big enough
For all your dreams and woes.
As you carry me, God carries you.
Together we learn and grow.

Mom and Dad are here to help.
To guide along the way.
Share the Heart of God with all
And, my goodness, remember to pray.

Love always,
Heart of God

Visit my website today to get your very own prayer pillow.
http://jacqies1234.wixsite.com/jacqiesnook

Notes of Gratitude From Jacqie

I am so thankful for the many ways that God has blessed me in my life.

It is my hope that children and their parents will be encouraged to learn more about the Heart of God through His Holy Word.

Thank you Holy Spirit for filling me up with a deep love for all people and a desire to share your heart with everyone.

I am eternally grateful to my husband and family for giving me the courage, or "push" to dive into this project.

To my nephews Ethan and Lincoln; thank you for your innocent, valuable input. Remember to keep your dreams big because our God is big and never give up!

Finally, to my daughter and to my son; thank you for showing enthusiasm and insight for each illustration. Your patience and kindness are appreciated.

I Love you Sweetie Pea and Bubber Woo.

HOLY SPIRIT

GOOD MORNING HOLY SPIRIT,
SHINING DOWN ON ME TODAY;
TO TEACH ME AND TO GUIDE ME
AS I LEARN FROM YOU TO PRAY.

YOU FILL MY HEAD WITH LAUGHTER,
AND KEEP MY HEART WITH JOY;
INHALING PEACE LIKE FRAGRANT AIR,
MY SOUL IT DOES REJOICE!

YOU COMFORT ME AND HOLD ME TIGHT,
YOU FILL ME UP WITH LOVE;
UNCONDITIONAL AND SO PURE,
FROM MY FATHER HIGH ABOVE.

JESUS SHED HIS BLOOD AT CALVARY,
ETERNITIES GREATEST GIFT.
AND AS IF THAT WERE NOT ENOUGH,
HE SENT YOU, HOLY SPIRIT,
FOR ALL MY BURDENS TO LIFT.

THE GUIDING LIGHT INSIDE ME,
SHINING BRIGHT FOR ALL TO SEE;
HOLY SPIRIT, YOU ARE MY EVERYTHING.
THE BEST FRIEND EVER GIVEN, JUST FOR ME.

About the Author/Illustrator

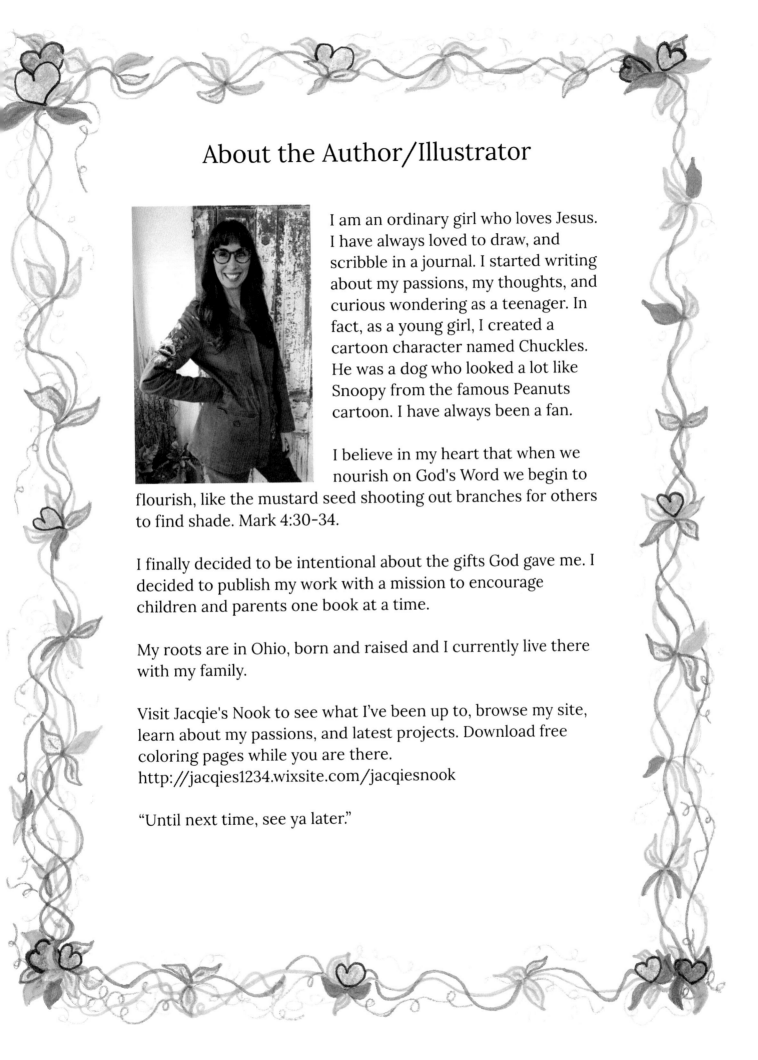

I am an ordinary girl who loves Jesus. I have always loved to draw, and scribble in a journal. I started writing about my passions, my thoughts, and curious wondering as a teenager. In fact, as a young girl, I created a cartoon character named Chuckles. He was a dog who looked a lot like Snoopy from the famous Peanuts cartoon. I have always been a fan.

I believe in my heart that when we nourish on God's Word we begin to flourish, like the mustard seed shooting out branches for others to find shade. Mark 4:30-34.

I finally decided to be intentional about the gifts God gave me. I decided to publish my work with a mission to encourage children and parents one book at a time.

My roots are in Ohio, born and raised and I currently live there with my family.

Visit Jacqie's Nook to see what I've been up to, browse my site, learn about my passions, and latest projects. Download free coloring pages while you are there.
http://jacqies1234.wixsite.com/jacqiesnook

"Until next time, see ya later."

Scripture Affirmations for Your Child

Dear Parents,

I put these **7 (seven)** scripture affirmations together for you to help you teach your children to make God's Word personal. God created the world in **7 (seven)** days, so I chose **7 (seven)** scriptures to get you started. Enjoy these scriptures with your child by confessing them out loud together.

GENESIS 1:27 So God created man in His own image; in the image of God He created him; Male and female He created them.

1. CONFESSION: God made me just like Him. He made me and I am just like Him.

1 JOHN 4: 7-8 Beloved, let us love one another, for love is of God, and everyone who loves is of God and knows God. Anyone who does not love does not know God, for God is love.

2. CONFESSION: I love everyone because love is of God. I am made by God and I know God. God is love.

LUKE 12: 6-7 Are not **5 (five)** sparrows sold for **2 (two)** pennies? Yet not **1 (one)** of them is forgotten by God. Indeed, even the hairs of your head are all numbered. Therefore do not fear. You are more valuable than many sparrows.

3. CONFESSION: God knows how many hairs are on my head. I am not afraid. I am valuable to God.

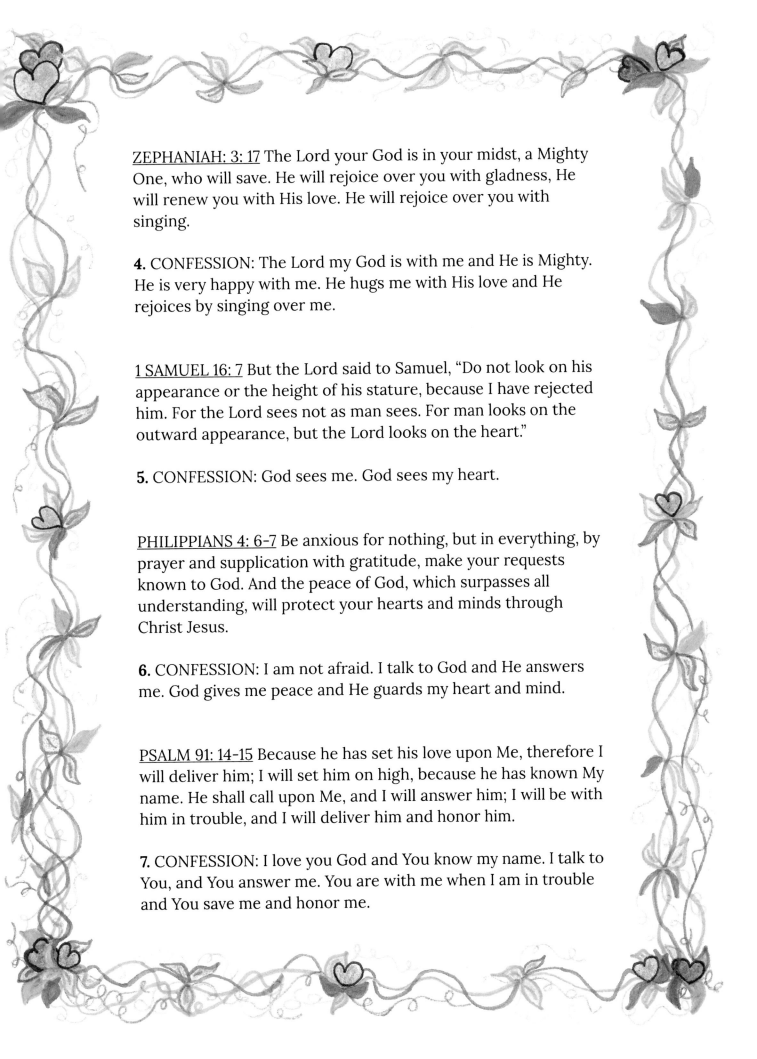

ZEPHANIAH: 3: 17 The Lord your God is in your midst, a Mighty One, who will save. He will rejoice over you with gladness, He will renew you with His love. He will rejoice over you with singing.

4. CONFESSION: The Lord my God is with me and He is Mighty. He is very happy with me. He hugs me with His love and He rejoices by singing over me.

1 SAMUEL 16: 7 But the Lord said to Samuel, "Do not look on his appearance or the height of his stature, because I have rejected him. For the Lord sees not as man sees. For man looks on the outward appearance, but the Lord looks on the heart."

5. CONFESSION: God sees me. God sees my heart.

PHILIPPIANS 4: 6-7 Be anxious for nothing, but in everything, by prayer and supplication with gratitude, make your requests known to God. And the peace of God, which surpasses all understanding, will protect your hearts and minds through Christ Jesus.

6. CONFESSION: I am not afraid. I talk to God and He answers me. God gives me peace and He guards my heart and mind.

PSALM 91: 14-15 Because he has set his love upon Me, therefore I will deliver him; I will set him on high, because he has known My name. He shall call upon Me, and I will answer him; I will be with him in trouble, and I will deliver him and honor him.

7. CONFESSION: I love you God and You know my name. I talk to You, and You answer me. You are with me when I am in trouble and You save me and honor me.

Can You Help?

Thank You For Reading My Book!

I really appreciate all of your feedback, and I love hearing what you have to say.

Please leave me an honest review on Amazon or Goodreads letting me know what you thought of the book.

As a fan, I value your opinion. I would love to know what Bible story is your favorite and which ones you would like to see next.

Thanks so much!

Send me an email at jacqies1234@gmail.com and join my fan club. I will send you a free gift and include you in the latest "scoop" about my future projects.

Be sure to visit my website for free coloring pages to download. http://jacqies1234.wixsite.com/jacqiesnook

Thank you for your support.
Jacqie D'Bach

Other Books by Jacqie D'Bach

SEDWIK ADVENTURES IN FRIENDSHIP
Ages 9-13
First in the series.

Parents and students will enjoy this refreshing telling of the Gospel, according to Sedwik. This unique donkey's-eye view introduces Jesus to the world in an unexpected, but highly relatable way. Characters are woven together from the Old and New Testaments encouraging a much deeper understanding of not only the purpose of Jesus life, death and resurrection, but also the relationship that He longs to have with each of us.

SOON TO COME:

STORIES FROM THE HEART OF GOD, ADAM AND EVE
Ages 0-5   Genesis Chapter 3
Counting and color recognition.

STORIES FROM THE HEART OF GOD, CAIN AND ABEL
Ages 0-5   Genesis Chapter 4
Alphabet recognition.

STORIES FROM THE HEART OF GOD, PSALM 23
Ages 0-5   Psalm 23
Encourages a growing, personal relationship with God.

Made in the USA
Monee, IL
07 September 2021